BASICS OF KEYBOARD THEORY

PREPARATORY LEVEL

Sixth Edition

Julie McIntosh Johnson

J. Johnson Music Publications

5062 Siesta Lane
Yorba Linda, CA 92886
Phone: (714) 961-0257
Fax: (714) 242-9350
www.bktmusic.com
info@bktmusic.com

Basics of Keyboard Theory, Preparatory Level, Sixth Edition

Published by:

J. Johnson Music Publications
5062 Siesta Lane.
Yorba Linda, CA 92886 U.S.A.
(714) 961-0257
www.bktmusic.com

©2014 by Julie McIntosh Johnson. Revised.
Previous editions ©1983, 1986, 1992 and 1998, 2007, Julie McIntosh Johnson.
Printed in United States of America

Library of Congress Cataloging in Publication Data

Johnson, Julie Anne McIntosh
Basics of Keyboard Theory, Preparatory Level, Sixth Edition

ISBN 10: 1-891757-00-8
ISBN 13: 978-1-891757-00-6

LC TX 4-721-499

Basics of Keyboard Theory, Preparatory Level corresponds with the MTAC Certificate of Merit™ Piano Syllabus. Certificate of Merit™ is an evaluation program of the Music Teachers' Association of California. Reference to 'Certificate of Merit™' (CM) does not imply endorsement by MTAC of this product.

TO THE TEACHER

Intended for group or private music lessons, *Basics of Keyboard Theory, Preparatory Level*, introduces the beginning music student to rudimentary theory concepts. It is intended for use by the student who has had about six months to one year of music lessons. It is assumed that the student knows the following:

1. Letter names of the treble clef and bass clef line and space notes.

2. Rhythms in 2/4, 3/4, and 4/4, using note and rest values of eighth, quarter, half, dotted half, and whole.

3. The names of the keys on the piano.

A great deal of time is spent on reading notes on the staff, because the student needs to be fairly fluent in these in order to understand the other theory concepts.

Basics of Keyboard Theory, Preparatory Level, is divided into 13 lessons, with Reviews of several of the lessons, and a Review Test at the end. Lessons may be divided into sections or combined with one another as needed, depending on the age and ability of the individual student. Whenever possible, it is helpful to demonstrate theory concepts on the keyboard, and apply them to the music the student is playing.

Learning music theory can be a very rewarding experience when carefully applied to lessons. *Basics of Keyboard Theory, Preparatory Level*, will give the student an important start on this valuable subject.

Also available from
J. Johnson Music Publications

Julie Johnson's Guide to
AP* Music Theory

by
Julie McIntosh Johnson
Author of *Basics of Keyboard Theory*

- Follows requirements of the College Board Advanced Placement* Music Theory exam
- Clear, easy to understand explanation of theory elements
- Application of concepts to musical excerpts
- Drills, analysis and multiple choice questions
- Ear training and sight singing with each lesson
- CD and answers included
- Purchase at your music store or order online

*AP and Advanced Placement are trademarks registered and/or owned by the College Board, which was not involved in the production of, and does not endorse, this product.

TABLE OF CONTENTS

Basics of Keyboard Theory is dedicated to my husband Rob,
without whose love, support, help, and incredible patience,
this series would not have been possible.

LESSON 1
THE GRAND STAFF

This is a **STAFF**. It has 5 lines and 4 spaces.

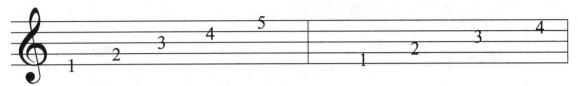

1. Number the lines and spaces on this staff.

This is a **TREBLE CLEF**.

It is also called the G clef.

The circle of the treble clef surrounds the second line of the staff. The second line is the note "G."

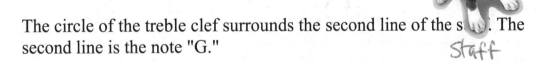

2. Draw 6 circles around the second line (the G line) on this staff. The first one is given.

2

3. Draw 5 more treble clefs below. (The first one is given.)

This is a **BASS CLEF**.

It is also called the F clef.

The two dots of the bass clef are above and below the fourth line of the staff. The fourth line is the note "F."

4. Draw dots above and below the fourth line (the F line) on the staff below. The first one is given.

5. Draw 5 more bass clefs on the staff below. (The first one is given.)

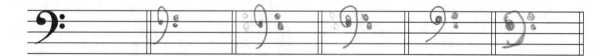

THE GRAND STAFF

To make a **GRAND STAFF**, begin by joining the treble and bass clefs with a **BAR** on their left side.

To finish the Grand Staff, a **DOUBLE BAR** (two bars) is placed on the right side, and a **BRACE** on the left.

6. Complete each Grand Staff by adding its missing part.

7. Make a Grand Staff out of each of the sets of staves below. Be sure to add all of the missing parts:

    1. Treble Clef
    2. Bass Clef
    3. Brace
    4. Double Bar

8. Match the symbols below with their names by drawing lines to connect them.

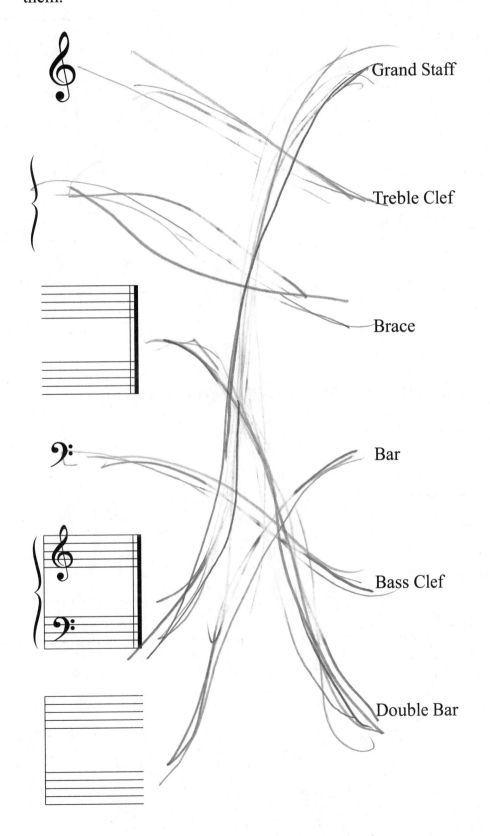

Grand Staff

Treble Clef

Brace

Bar

Bass Clef

Double Bar

This page has purposely been left blank.

LESSON 2
LINE NOTES AND SPACE NOTES

Musical notes come in many shapes. Whole notes are made of a cir
more information on whole notes, see Lesson 12.)

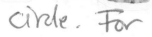
circle. For (handwritten)

WHOLE NOTE

Half notes and quarter notes each have a head (or circle) and a stem (a line attached to the note.) (For more information on half notes and quarter notes, see Lesson 12.)

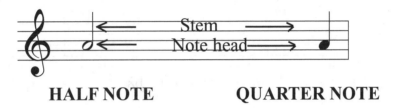

HALF NOTE   **QUARTER NOTE**

A **LINE NOTE** has a line going through its head.

LINE NOTES

The heads of **SPACE NOTES** are between two lines, or above and below a line. There is no line going through the head of a space note.

SPACE NOTES

1. Circle the line notes.

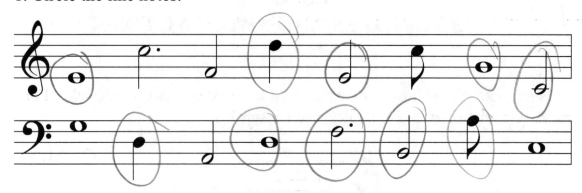

2. Circle the space notes.

3. Tell whether each of these notes is a line note or space note. Write "**L**" for line notes, and "**S**" for space notes.

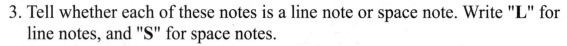

L   L   S   S   L   S   L   S

4. Draw a whole note on each line of this staff.

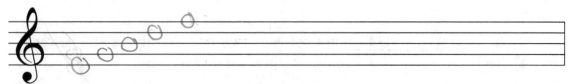

5. Draw a whole note on each space of this staff.

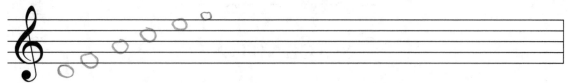

LESSON 3
LETTER NAMES OF TREBLE CLEF NOTES

These are the letter names of the space notes in the treble clef.

D F A C E G

1. Name these space notes.

C F E A C E D F G

A G C D C F E A D

2. Write these **SPACE** notes.

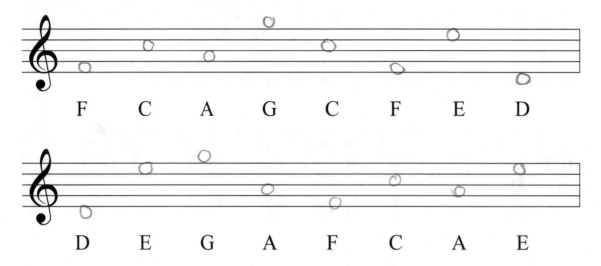

F   C   A   G   C   F   E   D

D   E   G   A   F   C   A   E

These are the letter names of the line notes in the treble clef.

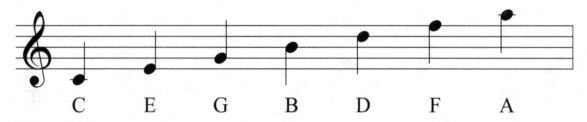

C   E   G   B   D   F   A

3. Name these line notes.

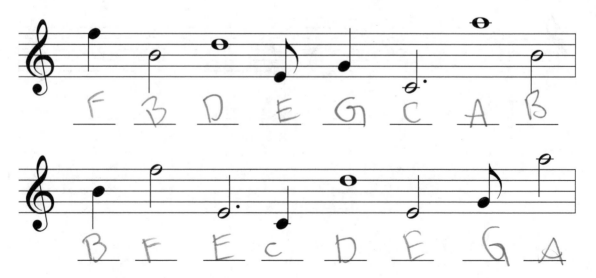

F   B   D   E   G   C   A   B

B   F   E   C   D   E   G   A

4. Write these **LINE** notes.

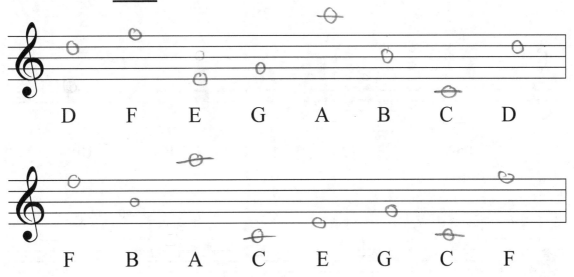

D F E G A B C D

F B A C E G C F

5. Name these notes. Each measure spells a word.

A C E   B E A D   F E E D

B A G   B E _   _ _ _

12

6. Write these notes.

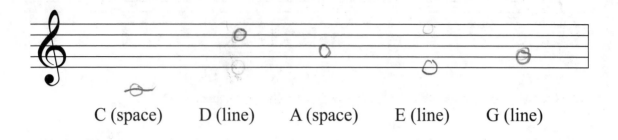

      C (space)   D (line)   A (space)   E (line)   G (line)

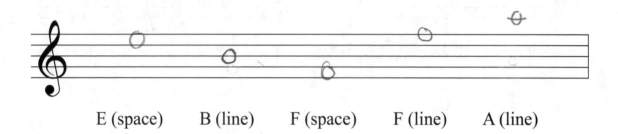

      E (space)   B (line)   F (space)   F (line)   A (line)

LESSON 4
LETTER NAMES OF BASS CLEF NOTES

These are the names of the space notes in the bass clef.

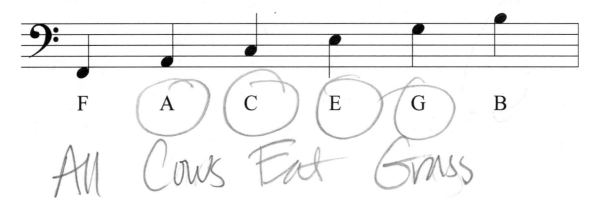

F A C E G B

All Cows Eat Grass

1. Name these space notes.

G C E A E B C E

E A E B G F C A

2. Write these **SPACE** notes.

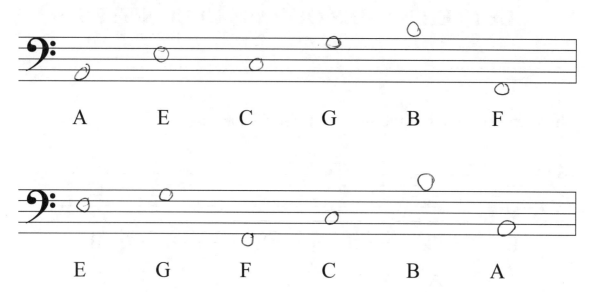

A   E   C   G   B   F

E   G   F   C   B   A

These are the names of the line notes in the bass clef.

E   G   B   D   F   A   C

Good Boys Do Fine Always

3. Name these line notes.

D   A   F   C   G   E   D   B

F   G   A   B   E   D   G   C

4. Write these **LINE** notes.

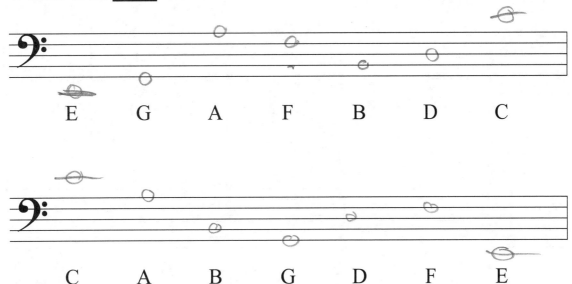

E   G   A   F   B   D   C

C   A   B   G   D   F   E

5. Name these notes. Each measure spells a word.

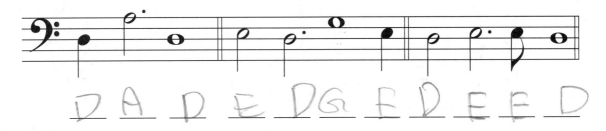

D A D E D G E D E E D

A D D B A D E G G

16

6. Write these notes.

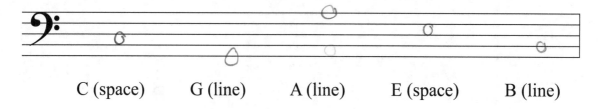

     C (space)   G (line)   A (line)   E (space)   B (line)

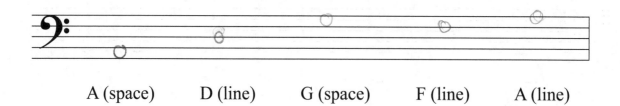

     A (space)   D (line)   G (space)   F (line)   A (line)

RH spaces : F A C E

LH spaces : All Cows Eat Grass

REVIEW
LETTER NAMES OF NOTES

RH lines : Every Good Bird Does Fly

LH lines : Good Boys Do Fine Always

1. Name these notes.

18

2. Write these notes on the staff, in **BOTH** clefs.

B   C   E   D   F   A   G   C

LESSON 5
SHARPS, FLATS, AND NATURALS

A **SHARP** (♯) raises a note. When you see a sharp in piano music, play the key to the **RIGHT** of the white key with the same letter name.

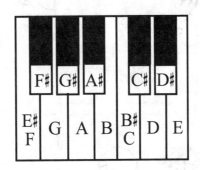

On the staff, a sharp is written to the **LEFT** of the note, and the center of the sharp is on the same line or space as the note head.

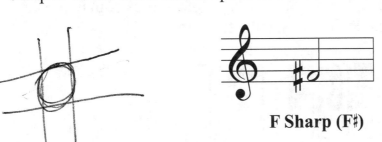

F Sharp (F♯)

1. Draw sharps to the **LEFT** of each of these notes. Be sure to put the center of each sharp on the same line or space as the note head. The first one is given.

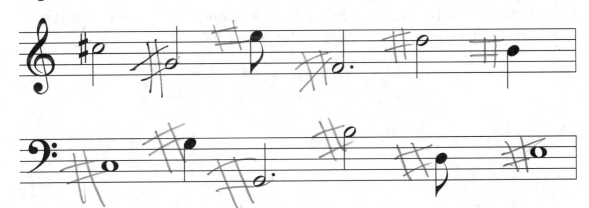

RH spaces: FACE

RH lines: Every Good Bird Does Fly

2. Name these notes. The first one is given.

A# | C# | G# | f# | D# | G# | f# | B#

G# | E# | G# | C# | f# | A# | B# | E#

A **FLAT** (♭) lowers a note. When you see a flat in piano music, play the key to the **LEFT** of the white key with the same letter name.

LH lines:
Great Big Dogs
Fight Animals

LH space: ACEG, All Cars Eat Gas

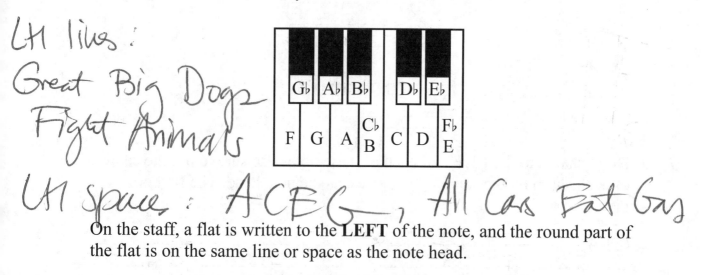

On the staff, a flat is written to the **LEFT** of the note, and the round part of the flat is on the same line or space as the note head.

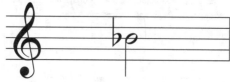

B Flat (B♭)

3. Draw flats to the **LEFT** of each of these notes. Be sure to put the round part of each flat on the same line or space as the note head. The first one is given.

4. Name these notes. The first one is given.

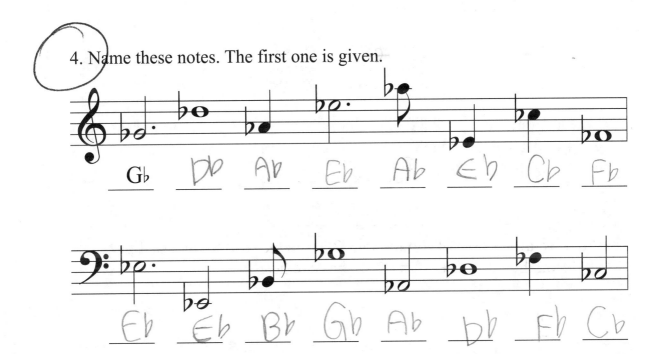

Gb   Db   Ab   Eb   Ab   Eb   Cb   Fb

Eb   Eb   Bb   Gb   Ab   Db   Fb   Cb

A **NATURAL** (♮) cancels a previous sharp or flat. On the piano, naturals are **WHITE** keys.

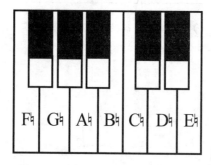

On the staff, a natural is written to the left of the note, and the center of the natural is on the same line or space as the note head.

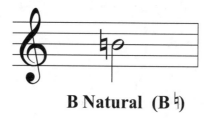

B Natural (B ♮)

5. Draw a natural to the **LEFT** of each of these notes. Be sure to put the center of each natural on the same line or space as the note head. The first one is given.

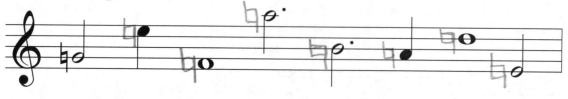

6. Name these notes. The first one is given.

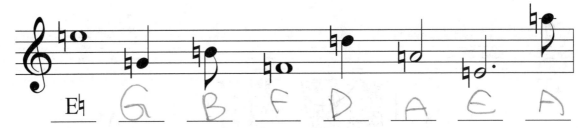

E♮   G   B   F   D   A   E   A

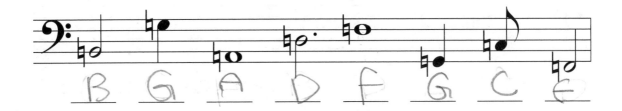

B   G   A   D   F   G   C   E

When a sharp, flat, or natural is written before a note, it is called an **ACCIDENTAL**.

7. Name these notes with their letter names and accidentals (♯, ♭, or ♮).

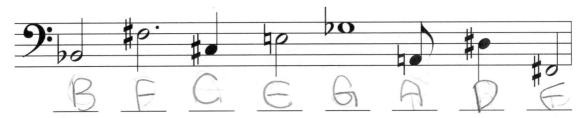

B   F   C   E   G   A   D   E

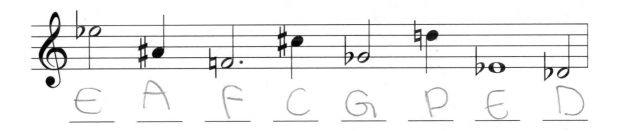

E   A   F   C   G   D   E   D

24

8. Write these notes.

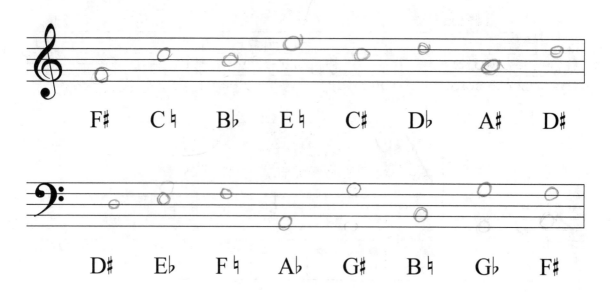

F♯ C♮ B♭ E♮ C♯ D♭ A♯ D♯

D♯ E♭ F♮ A♭ G♯ B♮ G♭ F♯

LESSON 6
HALF STEPS AND WHOLE STEPS

If you play two keys on the piano which are right next to each other (remember to consider the black keys), you are playing a **HALF-STEP.**

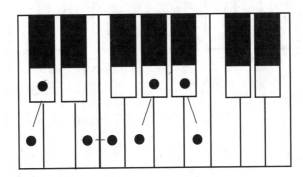

HALF-STEPS

A **WHOLE-STEP** skips one, and only one, key or note.

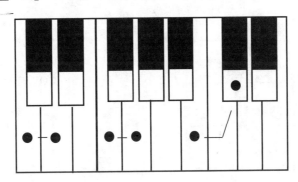

WHOLE-STEPS

1. Circle the half-steps below.

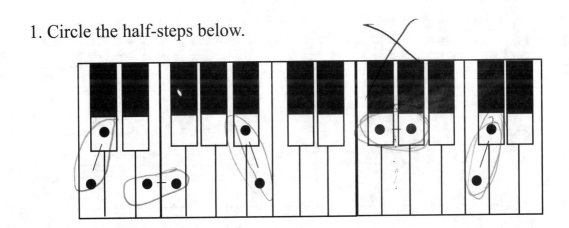

2. Circle the whole-steps below.

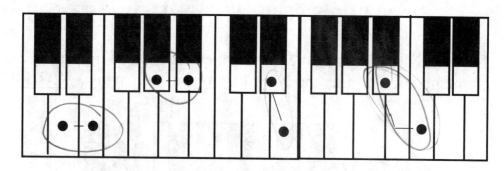

3. Tell whether these are whole-steps or half-steps. The first one is given.

D up to E   Whole   E up to F♯   whole

A up to B   whole   A♭ up to B♭   whole

E up to F   half   B♭ up to C   whole

(G♭ up to A♭)   half whole   (G down to F♯)   wholehalf

C down to B   half   F down to E   half

G up to A   whole   D down to C♯   half

4. Tell whether these are whole-steps or half-steps. The first one is given.

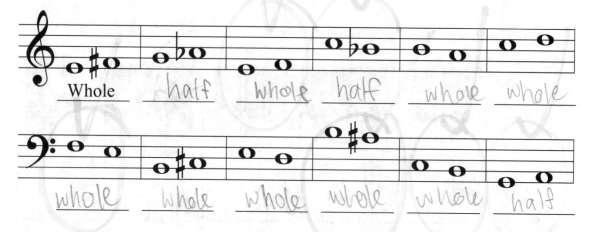

Whole   half   whole   half   whole   whole

whole   whole   whole   whole   whole   half

LESSON 7
INTERVALS

An **INTERVAL** is the distance between two notes. Intervals are named with numbers.

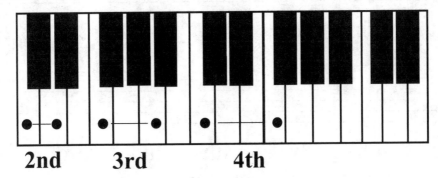

2nd   **3rd**   **4th**

When counting intervals on the staff, count the line or space on which each note sits, and all the lines or spaces between the two notes.

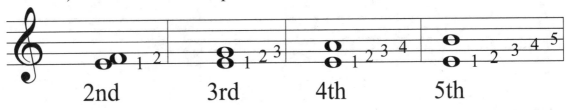

2nd   3rd   4th   5th

Intervals with **EVEN** numbers are made up of **ONE LINE NOTE** and **ONE SPACE NOTE.**

Intervals with **ODD** numbers are made up of **TWO LINE NOTES** or **TWO SPACE NOTES.**

1. Name these intervals. The first one is given.

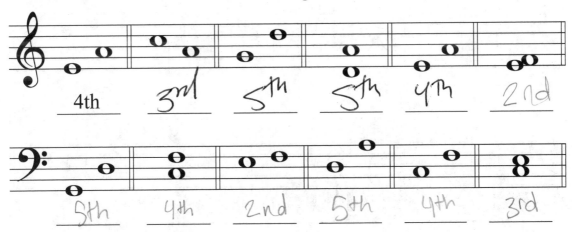

4th   3rd   5th   5th   4th   2nd

5th   4th   2nd   5th   4th   3rd

2. Write a note <u>above</u> the given note to complete these intervals. The first one is given.

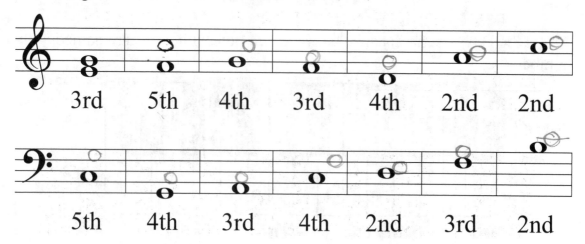

3rd   5th   4th   3rd   4th   2nd   2nd

5th   4th   3rd   4th   2nd   3rd   2nd

3. Name the given note in each of these measures. Then, write the second note of the interval, and name the second note. The first one is given.

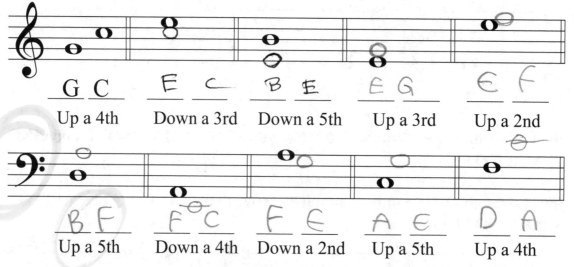

G C   E C   B E   E G   E F

Up a 4th   Down a 3rd   Down a 5th   Up a 3rd   Up a 2nd

B F   F C   F E   A E   D A

Up a 5th   Down a 4th   Down a 2nd   Up a 5th   Up a 4th

4. Tell what intervals are used in each of these measures. The first one is given.

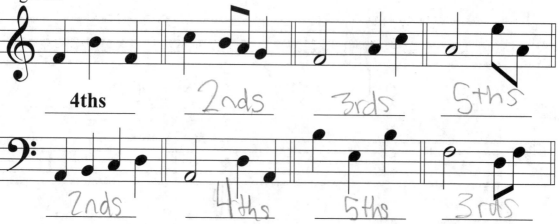

4ths   2nds   3rds   5ths

2nds   4ths   5ths   3rds

LESSON 8
C, F, G, AND D MAJOR
FIVE FINGER PATTERNS AND TRIADS

A **<u>FIVE FINGER PATTERN</u>** is created by placing all five fingers on five keys that are next to each other on the piano, using a specific pattern of whole steps and half steps.

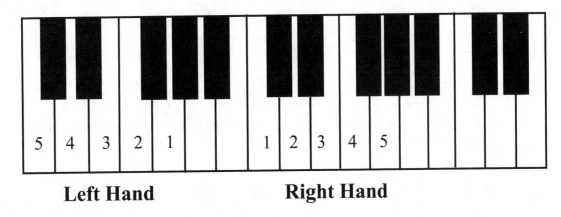

Left Hand   **Right Hand**

Some five finger patterns (or "five finger positions") have sharps or flats, and some do not. On the staff, a five finger pattern moves from a line note to a space note without skipping any lines or spaces. The lowest note of the five finger pattern gives the pattern its letter name.

C MAJOR   **D MAJOR**
FIVE FINGER PATTERN   **FIVE FINGER PATTERN**

30

1. Some of the examples below are five finger patterns, and some are not.
   Circle the ones that ARE five finger patterns.

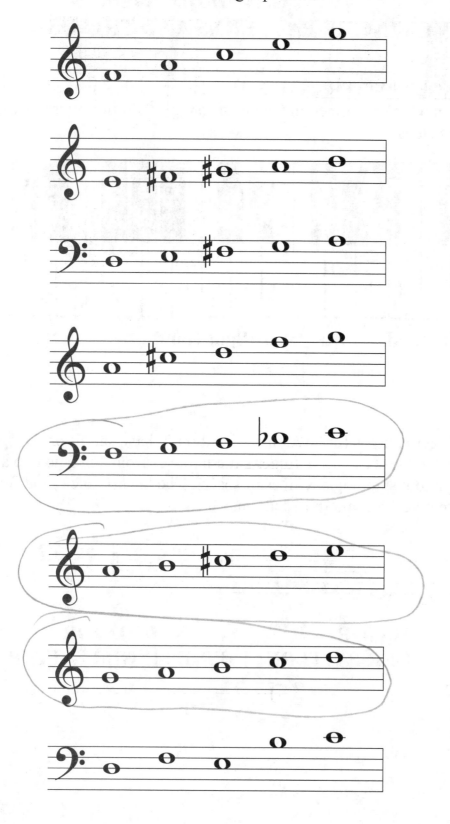

MAJOR FIVE FINGER PATTERNS have whole steps between all keys except keys 3 and 4, where there is a half step.

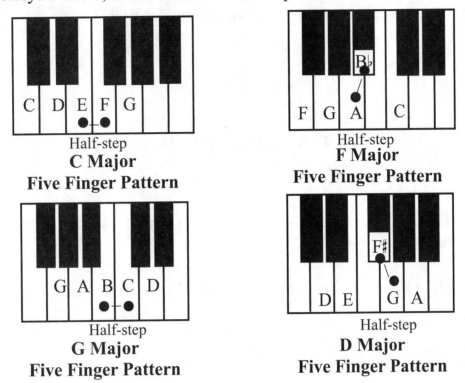

2. Match these five finger patterns with their names.

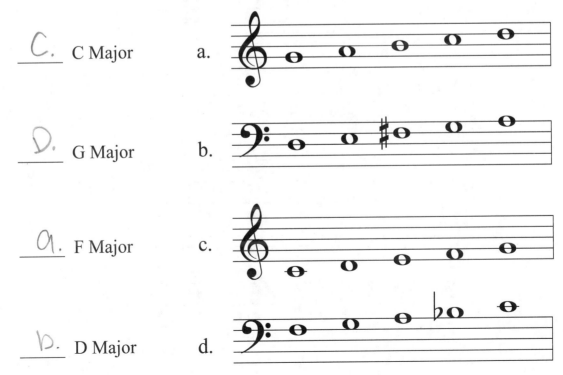

___C.___ C Major   a.

___D.___ G Major   b.

___a.___ F Major   c.

___b.___ D Major   d.

The first, third, and fifth notes of a five finger pattern, when played at the same time or one after another, make a **TRIAD**, or a chord with three notes. The lowest note of a triad gives it its letter name, or ROOT.

G MAJOR TRIAD

C, F, and G Major Triads each have three white keys. Find each of these triads on the piano.

D Major Triad has a sharp on the middle note (F♯). Find this triad on the piano.

3. Match these triads with their names.

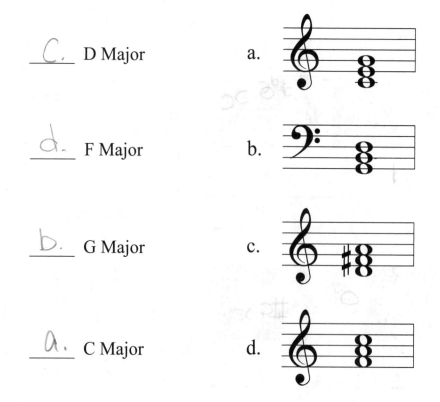

_C._ D Major   a.

_d._ F Major   b.

_b._ G Major   c.

_a._ C Major   d.

4. Write the letter names of the keys for these five finger patterns on the keyboards below. Circle the keys that make each triad.

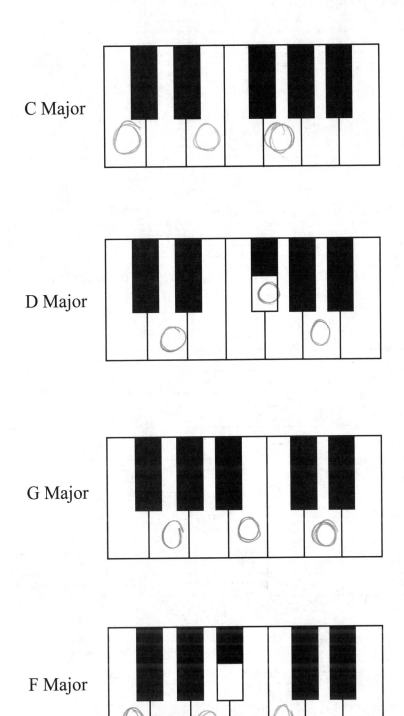

C Major

D Major

G Major

F Major

5. Write the notes for each of these five finger patterns and triads, in both clefs.

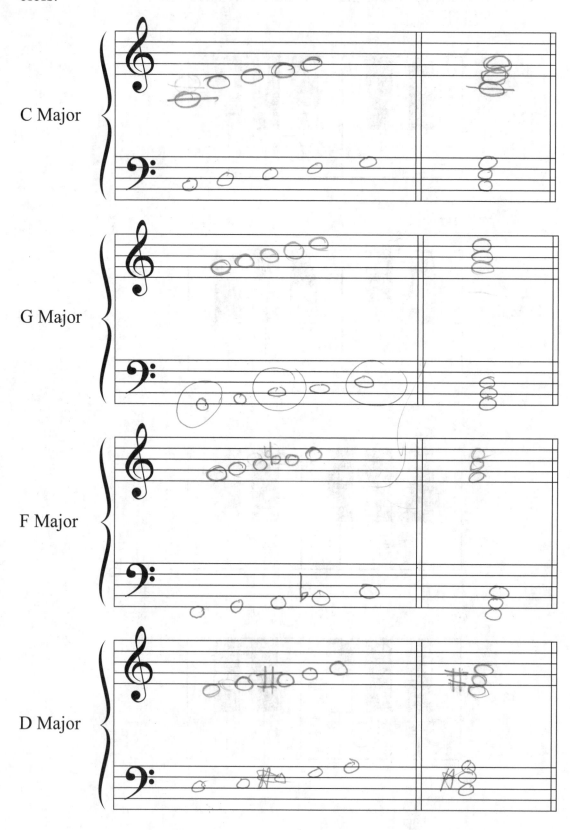

C Major

G Major

F Major

D Major

LESSON 9
C, F, G, AND D MINOR
FIVE FINGER PATTERNS AND TRIADS

To change a **MAJOR** five finger pattern to <u>MINOR</u>, the **MIDDLE** or **THIRD** note is **LOWERED A HALF STEP.**

G MAJOR FIVE FINGER PATTERN   **G MINOR FIVE FINGER PATTERN**

In **MINOR FIVE FINGER PATTERNS**, the whole steps occur between all notes except 2 and 3, where there is a half step.

As in Major five finger patterns, the minor triad is made up of the first, third, and fifth notes of the pattern, and the lowest note of the pattern names it.

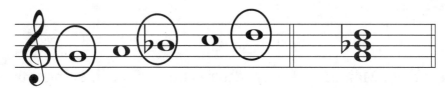

G MINOR FIVE FINGER PATTERN   **G MINOR TRIAD**

1. Write the letter names for each of these five finger patterns on the keyboards below. Circle the notes that make each triad.

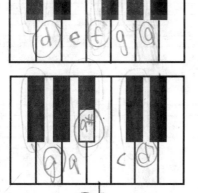

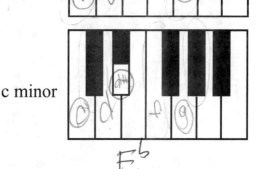

2. Match each of these minor five finger patterns with its name.

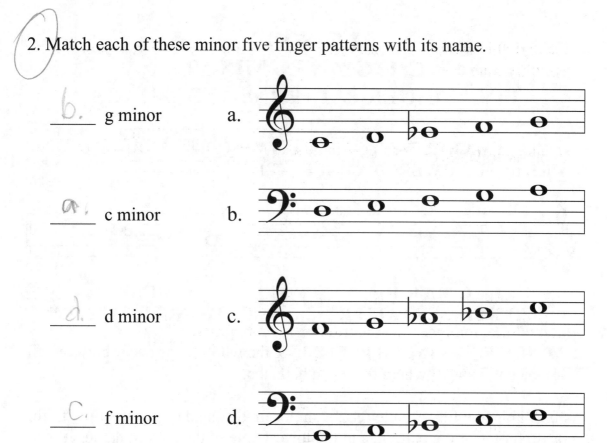

_b._   g minor   a.

_a._   c minor   b.

_d._   d minor   c.

_c._   f minor   d.

3. Change these Major five finger patterns into minor five finger patterns by putting a flat before the third note. Do not change any sharps or flats that are not on the third note.

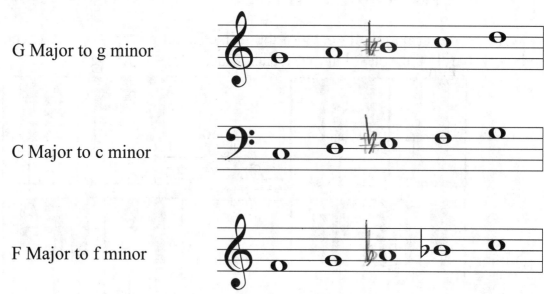

G Major to g minor

C Major to c minor

F Major to f minor

37

4. Change this minor five finger pattern into Major by placing a sharp before the third note.

d minor to D Major

5. Match these minor triads (chords) with their names.

_b_ g minor   a.

_d_ d minor   b.

_b_ c minor   c.

_a_ f minor   d.

6. Write each of these minor five finger patterns and their triads in both clefs.

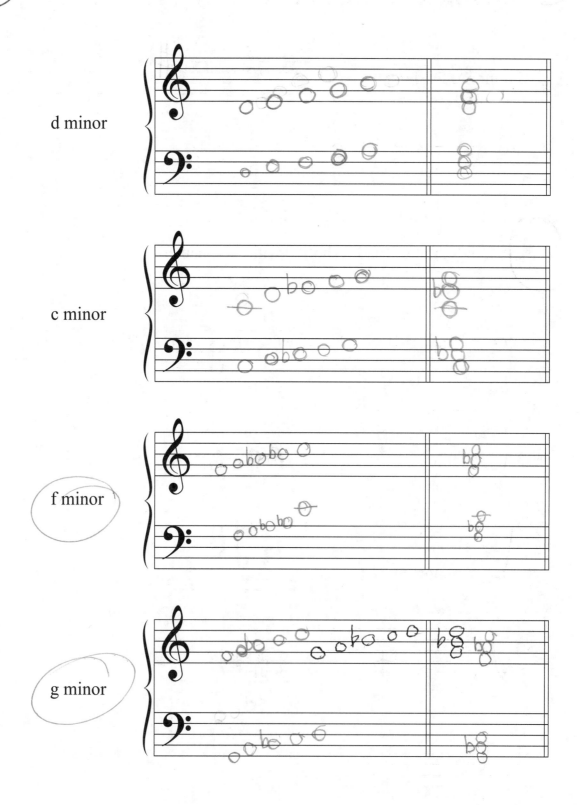

d minor

c minor

f minor

g minor

REVIEW
MAJOR AND MINOR FIVE FINGER PATTERNS

1. Name each of these five finger patterns with their letter names, and Major or minor.

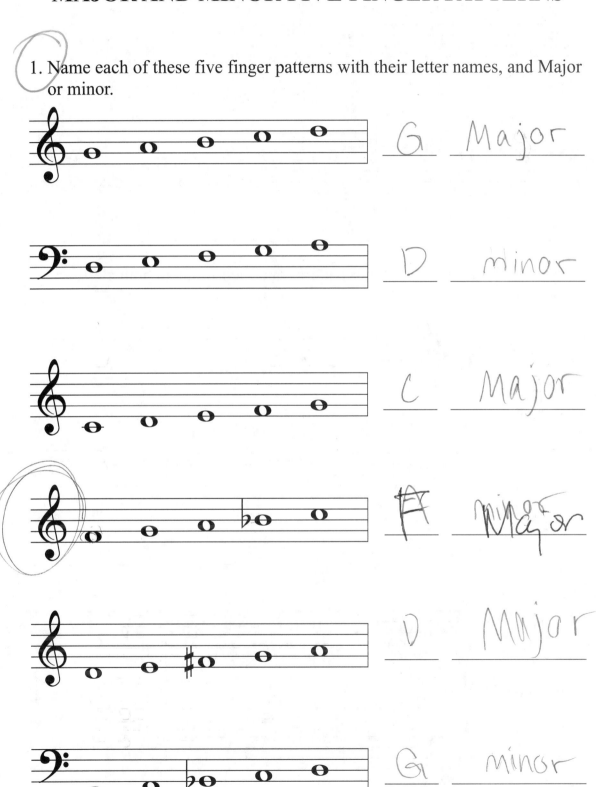

G Major

D minor

C Major

F̶ minor (Major)

D Major

G minor

40

(No. 1, continued.)

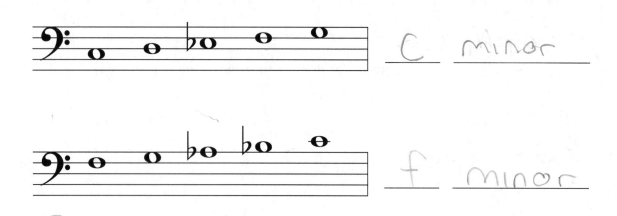

_C minor_____

_f minor_____

2. Write each of these five finger patterns and their triads in both clefs.

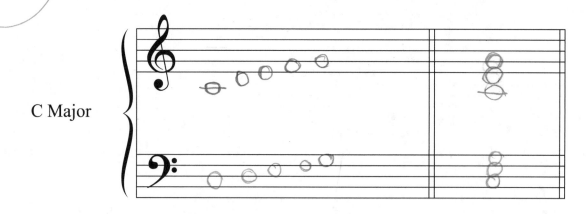

C Major

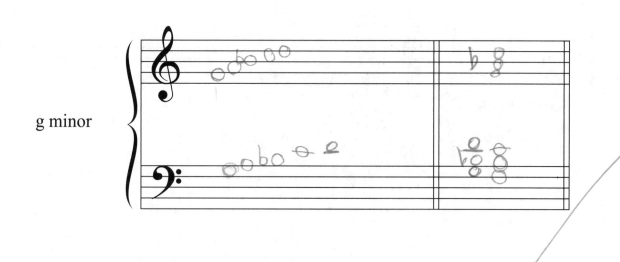

g minor

(No. 2, continued)

D Major
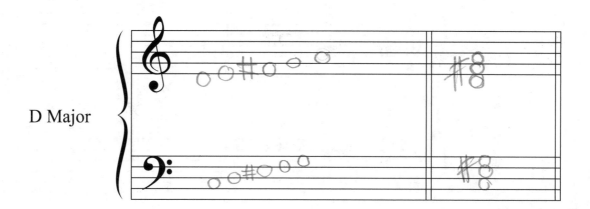

f minor
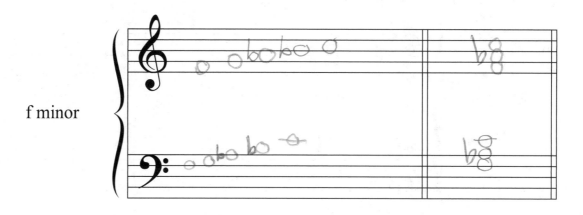

G Major
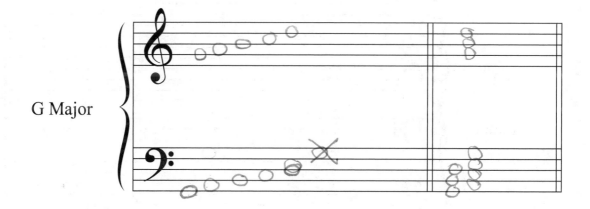

42

(No. 2, continued.)

F Major
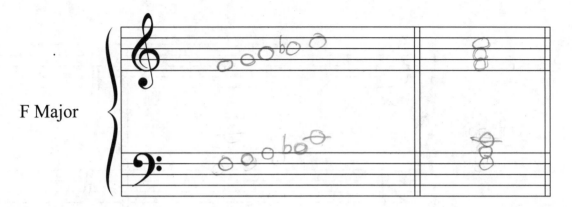

c minor
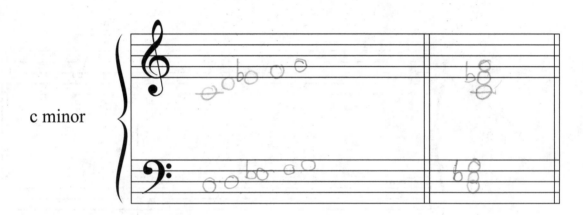

d minor
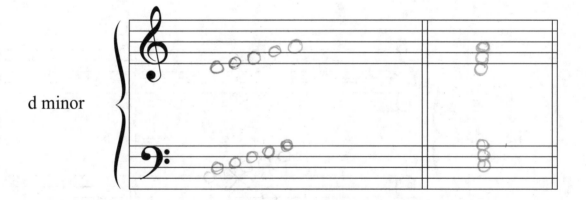

REVIEW
LESSONS 1-9

1. Add the missing part to complete each Grand Staff.

2. Name these notes.

C   d   F   G   Bb   C   Eb

GF   C   Ab   Bb   E   F#   AE

3. Tell whether these are whole steps or half steps.

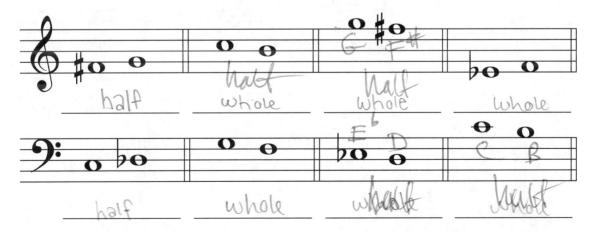

half   half whole   half whole   whole

G# F#

half   whole   whole half   half

Eb D   C B

44

4. Name these intervals. The first one is given.

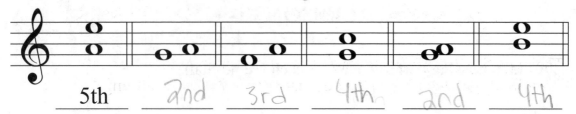

    5th   2nd   3rd   4th   2nd   4th

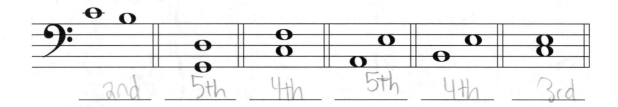

    2nd   5th   4th   5th   4th   3rd

5. Write these five finger patterns and triads.

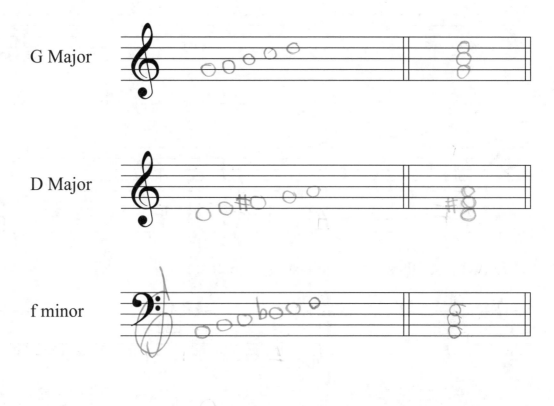

G Major

D Major

f minor

c minor

45

LESSON 10
C, F, AND G MAJOR KEY SIGNATURES

The **KEY SIGNATURE** is found at the beginning of the music, to the right of the clef signs. The key signature indicates two things:

   1. The **KEY** or **TONALITY** of the music.

   2. Which notes in the music are to receive sharps or flats.

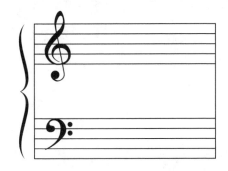

C MAJOR KEY SIGNATURE

NO SHARPS OR FLATS

G MAJOR KEY SIGNATURE: **F♯**

ALL F's ARE PLAYED AS F♯

F MAJOR KEY SIGNATURE: **B♭**

ALL B's ARE PLAYED AS B♭

1. Match these Major key signatures with their names by drawing lines to connect them.

C Major

G Major

F Major

2. Name the sharp or flat used in each of these key signatures, then name the Major key.

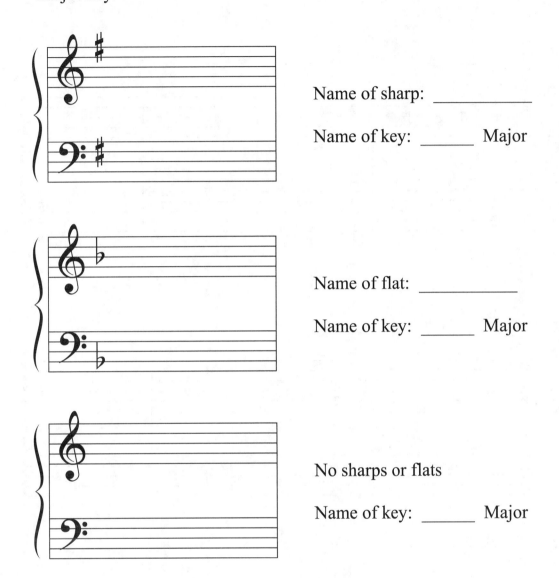

Name of sharp: _____

Name of key: _____ Major

Name of flat: _____

Name of key: _____ Major

No sharps or flats

Name of key: _____ Major

3. Write the key signature for each of these keys.

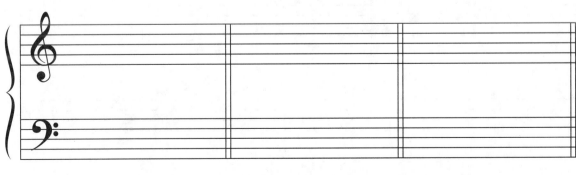

C Major   **F Major**   **G Major**

4. Write the name of the key for each of the following musical examples.

a. Key of _____ Major

b. Key of _____ Major

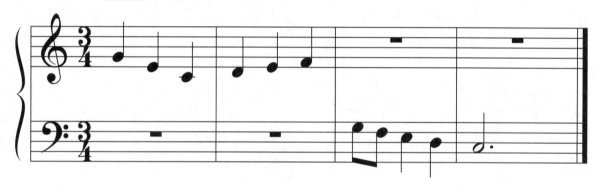

c. Key of _____ Major

LESSON 11
C, F, AND G MAJOR SCALES

MAJOR SCALES contain 8 notes.

C MAJOR SCALE

Major Scales begin and end on notes which have the same letter names. They have the same flats or sharps as the Major key signature with the same name.

C Major scale has no sharps or flats.
F Major scale has B♭.
G Major scale has F♯.

Whole steps occur between most of the notes, with half steps between notes 3-4 and notes 7-8.

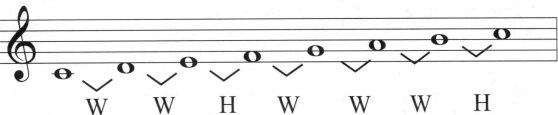

1. Mark the whole steps and half steps in these Major Scales. The first one is given.

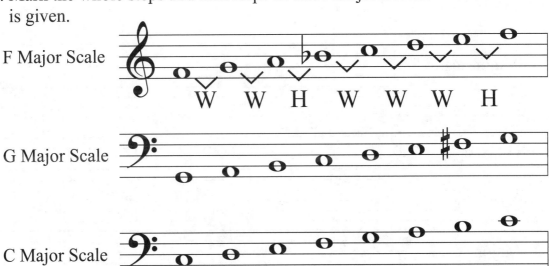

50

(No. 1, continued)

G Major Scale

F Major Scale

C Major Scale

2. Write these Major Scales.

C Major Scale

G Major Scale

F Major Scale

G Major Scale

F Major Scale

C Major Scale

LESSON 12
TIME SIGNATURES AND RHYTHM

The **TIME SIGNATURE** for a musical composition is found at the beginning of the music, next to the clef signs.

TIME SIGNATURE: $\frac{2}{4}$

The top number of the time signature tells how many beats are in each measure.

$\frac{2}{4}$ = Two (2) beats (or counts) per measure

The bottom number of the time signature tells which type of note receives one beat or count.

$\frac{2}{4}$ = Quarter note (♩) receives one beat (or count)

52

If the bottom number of a time signature is a 4, these notes receive the following number of beats or counts (other types of counting are possible):

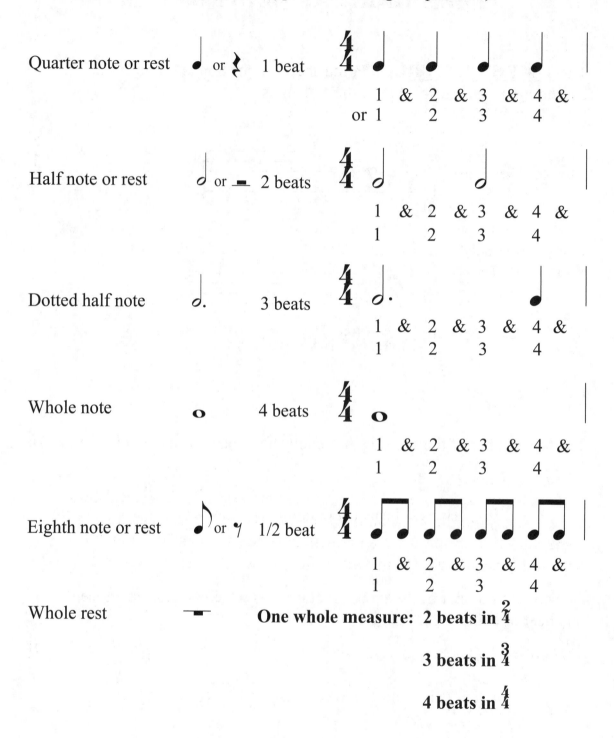

In $\frac{2}{4}$, the first beat of each measure is the strongest.

In $\frac{3}{4}$, the first beat of each measure is strongest.

In $\frac{4}{4}$, the first beat of each measure is strongest, and the third beat is also slightly emphasized.

(The accents in the above examples are only meant to indicate strong and weak beats. They are not intended to imply that each strong beat receives an accent.)

When writing numbers for the beats or counts under the notes of a musical phrase, begin each complete measure with the number 1. Write numbers under the appropriate notes until the top number of the key signature is reached. (For example, music in $\frac{3}{4}$ will have the numbers 1, 2, and 3 in each measure.) Begin the new measure with the number 1.

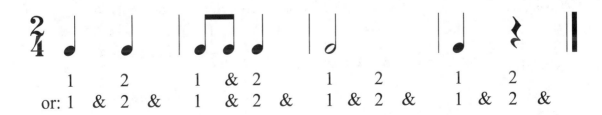

54

1. Fill in the missing words.

2 = 2 _____ per measure, emphasize beat _____
4 = Quarter note receives _____ beat or count

3 = _____ beats per measure, emphasize beat _____
4 = Quarter note receives _____ beat or count

4 = 4 beats per _____ emphasize beats _____ and _____
4 = _____ note receives _____ beat or count

2. Tell how many beats each of these notes receives in $\frac{2}{4}$, $\frac{3}{4}$ or $\frac{4}{4}$ time.

♪ = _____ beat

♩ = _____ beat

𝅗𝅥 = _____ beats

𝅗𝅥. = _____ beats

3. Write the counts for these rhythms, and place accents on the beats which will be emphasized. (The first measure is given.)

(3, continued)

4. Write the counts for these musical examples, and place accents on the beats which are to be emphasized. The first one is given.

5. Write the name for each of these notes and rests. The first one is given.

♩   Quarter note _____

𝅗𝅥   _____

▬   _____

𝄾   _____

𝅝   _____

♪   _____

𝄽   _____

▬   _____

𝅗𝅥.   _____

6. Match each note with the rest that has the same number of beats.

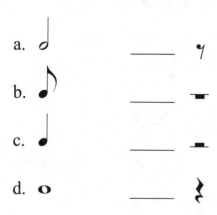

a. 𝅗𝅥   _____ 𝄾

b. ♪   _____ ▬

c. ♩   _____ ▬

d. 𝅝   _____ 𝄽

LESSON 13
SIGNS AND TERMS

The following symbols and terms may appear in music you are learning.

1. *a tempo:* return to the original tempo (the speed at which the piece began)

2. 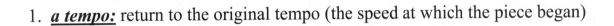 **accent:** play the note louder than the others

3. *D.C. al fine (Da Capo al fine)*:return to the beginning of the music and play until the word *fine*

4. **dynamics:** symbols or terms that indicate varying degrees of loud or soft (such as *p* or *f*)

5. *fermata:* hold the note longer than its value

6. *f* *forte:* loud

7. **slur:** curved line indicating to connect the notes; play smoothly or *legato*

8. *p* *piano:* soft

9. **repeat sign:** repeat the music.

10. *rit., ritard., ritardando:* gradually slower

11. *staccato:* detached or crisp

12. **tie:** do not play the second note; hold it

1. Match these signs and terms with their definitions.

_____   (notation: four notes under a slur)   a. *staccato:* detached

                                                                 b. *piano:* soft

_____   (notation: two notes with a tie)   c. tie: hold the second note

                                                                  d. slur:curved line indicating to play *legato* (connect the notes)

_____   (notation: staccato note)   e. *forte:* loud

_____   *p*   f. *Da Capo al fine:* return to the beginning and play to *fine*

_____   (repeat signs)   g. *ritardando:* gradually slower

_____   *f*   h. repeat sign: repeat the music

_____   (accented note)   i. accent: play the note louder than the others

_____   *D.C. al fine*   j. return to the original tempo

_____   (fermata note)   k. *fermata:* hold the note longer than its value

_____   *rit.*

_____   *a tempo*

_____   dynamics   l. symbols or terms that indicate varying degrees of loud or soft

REVIEW
LESSONS 10-13

1. Write the counts for these rhythms, and place accents on the beats which are to be emphasized.

a.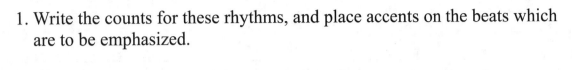

b.

c.

2. Write the meanings of these signs and terms.

a. *a tempo* _____

b.  _____

c. _____

d. *rit.* _____

e.

f.

g. *f* _____

h.

i. *p* _____

j.

k. *D.C. al fine* _____

3. Complete these scales by adding a sharp or flat, if necessary.

a.

F Major

b.

G Major

c.

C Major

Score: _____   **REVIEW TEST**   Perfect Score: 45
Passing Score: 31

1. a. Put an X on the A key. (3 points)
   Put a check (√) on the A♭ key.

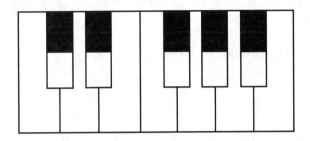

   b. Is A to A♭ a half step? _____ Yes   _____ No

2. a. Put an X on the D key. (3 points)
   Put a check on the E♭ key.

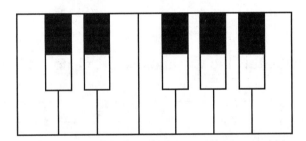

   b. Is D to E♭ a whole step? _____ Yes   _____ No

3. a. Put an X on the F key. (3 points)
   Put a check on the E♭ key.

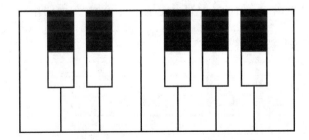

   b. Is F to E♭ a half step? _____ Yes   _____ No

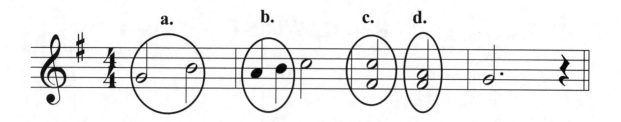

4. Give the number name of the intervals that are circled in the music above. The first one is given. (3 points)

a. __3rd__   b. _____   c. _____   d. _____

5. a. Add the flat (♭) that will make this the F Major Scale. (1 point)

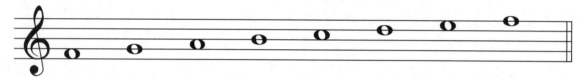

b. Add the sharp (♯) that will make this the G Major Scale. (1 point)

6. Circle the three Major triads in this example. (Circle the notes on the staff.) (3 points)

7. Tell how many beats or counts each of these notes will receive when a quarter note receives one beat or count (such as in $\frac{2}{4}$, $\frac{3}{4}$, or $\frac{4}{4}$). The first one is given. (4 points)

___2___   _____   _____   _____   _____

8. Match the musical example with the correct word. Put the number of the example next to the word. (7 points)

1.

_____ accent

2.

_____ tie

_____ *piano:* soft

3.

_____ slur: play smoothly or *legato*

4. *p*

_____ repeat sign

5.

_____ *fermata*

6. *f*

_____ *forte:* loud

7.

64

9. The following example is *Hot Cross Buns.* Answer the questions about
the music. (5 points)

a. How many beats (counts) are in each measure? _____

b. Check the note that receives one beat or count.

c. How many quarter notes are in the music? _____

d. Name the measure that is different from the others. _____

e. How many notes are marked staccato? _____

10. This example is from *Twinkle Twinkle Little Star*. Answer the questions about the music. (4 points)

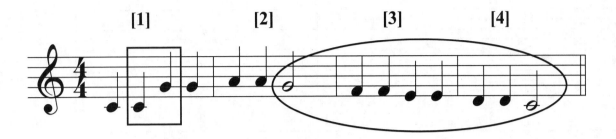

a. How many beats (counts) are in each measure? _____

b. Check the note that receives one beat (count).

c. Name the five finger pattern that is circled at the end of the piece, and tell whether it is Major or minor.

_____   _____

d. Name the interval that has a box around it at the beginning of the piece.

_____

66

11. Answer the questions about this music. (8 points)

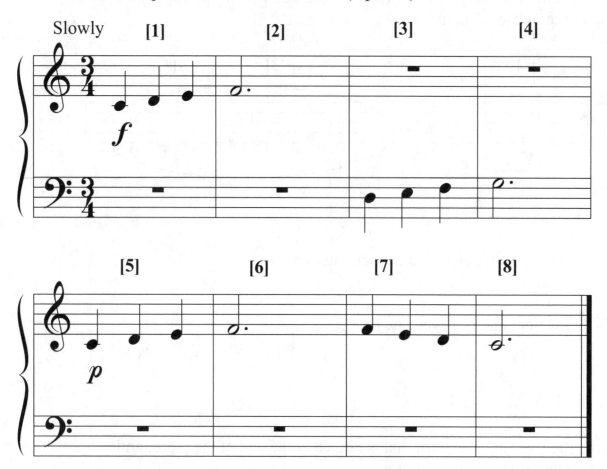

a. Name the first note in the right hand part. _____

b. Name the first note in the left hand part. _____

c. Name the last note of the piece. _____

d. What intervals are used in measure 1? _____

e. How many beats (counts) are in each measure? _____

f. How should the piece be played? (Circle the answer.)

        Quickly   Slowly

g. What does the sign *f* mean? _____

h. What does the sign *p* mean? _____

Basics of Keyboard Theory and Guide to AP Theory
ORDER FORM

NAME_____

ADDRESS_____

CITY_____STATE_____ZIP_____

PHONE_____E-MAIL_____

QTY	ITEM	COST	TOTAL
	Preparatory Level	9.50	
	Level 1	9.50	
	Level 2	9.50	
	Level 3	9.95	
	Level 4	9.95	
	Level 5	10.50	
	Level 6	10.50	
	Level 7	10.95	
	Level 8	11.95	
	Level 9	12.95	
	Level 10	12.50	
	Answer Book, Levels P-10	11.95	
	Julie Johnson's Guide to AP Music Theory	39.95	

	Sub-Total	
	Calif. Residents: Sales Tax	
	Shipping	
	TOTAL	

Shipping Rates:
  1-5 Items.........$5.00
  6-10 Items.......$6.00
  11 or more.......$7.00

Order online, or mail form with payment. Make checks payable to:

J. Johnson Music Publications
5062 Siesta Lane
Yorba Linda, CA 92886
714-961-0257   Fax: 714-242-9350
www.bktmusic.com   info@bktmusic.com
Prices subject to change. Check www.bktmusic.com for current information.